WHO LIKES THE SUN?

Who Likes the Sun?

BY BEATRICE SCHENK DE REGNIERS

WITH WOODCUTS BY LEONA PIERCE

HARCOURT, BRACE & WORLD, INC., NEW YORK

Let me tell you about the sun.

When the sun is outside
and I am inside
in the morning early,
the sun sends me a letter,
the sun sends me a message.
A square of sunlight on the floor—
a sparkle of sunlight on the wall—
it is a message from the sun.
And it says,
　　　Good morning,
it says,
　　　Get up,
it says,
　　　Come out and play.

This is how we play.
I stand in the sunlight,
and because I am standing in the sunlight,
I have a shadow.
I try to step on my shadow, but I cannot step on it.
I turn and try to run away.
I chase my shadow.
My shadow chases me.
And that is how we play the shadow game.

The dog has his dog-shadow.
The cat has her cat-shadow.
Here is a flower in the sunlight,
and the sun gives it a flower-shadow.
Even a bug—a tiny little bug—
has a little bug-shadow of his own.

I look up to the sun
and I want to say, "Thank you, sun,
for the shadow game."
But the sun is so dazzling, the sun is so bright,
I just close my eyes.
Then I feel the sun warm on my face, and
I hold my face up to the sun
and it feels good.

When I am in the sun a while,
I put my hand on my head and my hair feels warm
like warm grass.

When the pussycat purrs in the sun and I pet her,
her fur feels warm—
like my warm hair,
like the warm grass.

I am on the sand at the beach.
The sun makes the sand warm,
and my two feet on the warm sand
are like two warm pieces of toast.

The sun makes the sand warm and warmer and hot and hotter!
I say "OUCH" when I put my bare feet on the sand.
The sand is so hot I cannot walk on it with my bare feet.
And I think,
"That is a trick the hot sun played.
What a sunny joke!"

Do you know what sunlight smells like?
On a sunny summer day
when the sunlight warms the grass
and the flowers and the earth,
take a deep breath
and smell the special smell of earth and flowers and grass
and sunlight.

Sometimes I am sick and I have to stay in bed.
Then when the sun comes in,
when the sun sends me a sunlight message
on the floor, on the wall,
I play tricks with the sun.
My mother gives me a mirror,
and I move my mirror in the sunlight.
I catch the sunlight in my mirror
and make the sun dance in my room—
along the walls, across the ceiling,
over my bed, the chair, the elephant,
my little good-luck toy elephant.
My mother comes into the room,
and I make the sun dance
on her nose.
I think that is very funny.
Sometimes my mother thinks it is funny too.

Who likes the sun?
The sunflower likes the sun.
Wherever the sun goes,
the sunflower turns its sunny face to watch.
The pussycat likes the sun.
Wherever there is a sunny spot,
the pussycat will find it
and sit in it.
The butterfly likes the sun too.
Her wings spink and shimmer in the sunlight.
And birds like the sun.
Some birds take a dust bath
in the sun-warm dust.

I like the sun.

There is a golden time of day,
in the afternoon,
just before the sun goes away,
when the sunlight makes everything look golden.
A woman is standing in the shade, holding a bag of groceries.
She crosses the street and moves into the sunlight,
and all of a sudden she looks beautiful
because the golden sunlight is on her hair
and on her face
and on her clothes.

This is the golden time of day.

When I am feeling specially happy about the sun,
I have a sun song,
a crazy little sun song,
that I sing to the sun.
No one has ever heard me sing it.
It is a secret between me and the sun,
but I will tell it to you.

This is how the sun song goes.
This is the crazy song I like to sing
to the sun.
Maybe you will want to sing it too.

Sun oh sun
oh sunny sun!
Sun oh fun
oh funny sun.
Fun oh hon
oh honey
funny
sunny
bunny
sun!

Maybe you would like to make up your own
secret sun song.
Then you can sing it to the sun. It will be
a secret between the sun and you.